M000117170

CURTAINS!

FAMILIAR PLAYS FOR LITTLE ACTORS

Adapted
by
Diane
Head

Fearon Teacher Aids
A Division of Frank Schaffer Publications, Inc.

Dedicated to

the hard-working, professional staff of Title One and Reading Recovery teachers in the Lewisville Independent School District of Lewisville, Texas

Editorial Director: Kristin Eclov

Editor: Lisa Schwimmer Marier

Inside and Cover Design: RedLane Studio

Inside and Cover Illustration: FAB Artists

Fearon Teacher Aids products were formerly manufactured and distributed by American Teaching Aids, Inc., a subsidiary of Silver Burdett Ginn, and are now manufactured and distributed by Frank Schaffer Publications, Inc. FEARON, FEARON TEACHER AIDS, and the FEARON balloon logo are marks used under license from Simon & Schuster, Inc.

Fearon Teacher Aids

A Division of Frank Schaffer Publications, Inc.
23740 Hawthorne Boulevard
Torrance, CA 90505

© 1999 Fearon Teacher Aids. All rights reserved. Printed in the United States of America. This publication, or parts thereof, may not be reproduced in any form by photographic, electronic, mechanical, or any other method, for any use, including information storage and retrieval, without written permission from the publisher. Student reproducibles excepted.

Contents

Introduction

Drama is a strong incentive for young readers—especially if they are actors!

CURTAINS! Familiar Plays for Little Actors is a collection of nine familiar fairy tales adapted into simple plays for emergent readers. The plays are designed for small groups in grades K–2, and are especially useful for teachers of specialized reading programs. The plays are best with four to ten children and one proficient reader as narrator—a parent, teacher, or older child.

At the beginning of each script is a word list to assist you in placing students in suitable plays. All words are listed, excluding those spoken by the narrator.

Try your hand at reader's theater, providing chairs and scripts for all actors. Or put on puppet plays or live performances! Stage directions are not included, as they would be inappropriate for children's reading levels. Encourage children to decide on their own stage directions and props.

There is no better way to build self-esteem, fluency, comprehension, parent cooperation, and a love of literature in your students than the performing arts.

Have a blast!

The Enormous Turnip

© Fearon Teacher Aids FE11001

Reproducible

The Enormous Turnip

Word List

a	get	not	try
all	girl	of	turnip
am	grow	oh	turnips
an	growing	old	up
and	have	one	us
are	help	only	we
back	huge	please	well
been	I	pull	were
before	if	pulling	what
biggest	is	put	when
can	it	right	why
cat	it's	seen	will
come	just	show	woman
course	kidding	stuck	won't
decided	let's	talk	wow
didn't	little	talks	yes
dog	long	thank	you
eat	man	the	
end	me	them	
enormous	more	this	
ever	mouse	thought	
for	move	time	
friend	my	to	
	narrator	too	
	need		
	no		

The Enormous Turnip

Characters

Narrator	Girl
Old Man	Dog
Turnip	Cat
Old Woman	Mouse

Suggested Props

seeds
pie plate

Narrator: Once upon a time, an old man decided he needed a taste of turnip pie. The problem was the old man didn't have any turnips—only seeds, which he planted.

Old Man: Grow, turnips!

Turnip: I AM growing!

Narrator: The old man took very good care of the turnip patch. He weeded and watered and watched, expecting to see hundreds of turnips one day. Unfortunately, only one turnip sprouted.

Old Man: Only one?

Turnip: Yes. Just me.

Narrator: Yes, but it was an enormous turnip. The old man saw that, indeed, the turnip was going to be really, really big. The time came for him to pull the turnip.

Old Man: I will pull the turnip.

Turnip: Oh, no you won't!

Narrator: Try as he might, he could not pull the enormous turnip. It was at that moment the turnip decided not to speak to the old man. He thought the man was his friend. Now he knew better.

Old Man: It's stuck!

Narrator: An old woman walked by.

Old Man: Old woman? Will you help me pull this turnip?

Old Woman: All right.

Old Man: I will pull the turnip and you pull me.

Narrator: The old man pulled the turnip and the old woman pulled the old man. They pulled and pulled, but the turnip didn't budge.

Turnip: I will show them.

Old Man: It won't move.

Old Woman: You are right. Let's get help.

Narrator: Just then, a little girl walked by.

Old Man: Little girl? Will you help us pull this turnip?

Old Woman: We have been pulling for a long time.

Girl: All right.

Old Man: I will pull the turnip.

Old Woman: I will pull the old man and you pull me.

Narrator: Together they pulled on the turnip. They pulled and pulled, but the turnip would not move.

Turnip: I will show them.

Old Man: It won't move.

Old Woman: You are right. Let's get more help.

Narrator: At that moment, a dog walked by.

Old Man: Dog? Will you help us pull this turnip?

Old Woman: We have been pulling for a long time.

Girl: It won't come up.

Dog: All right.

Old Man: I will pull the turnip.

Old Woman: I will pull the old man.

Girl: I will pull the old woman and you pull me.

Narrator: So they tried again. They pulled and pulled until their hands were sore, but the turnip was stuck fast in the ground.

Turnip: I will show them.

Old Man: It won't move.

Old Woman: You are right. Let's get more help.

Narrator: At that moment, a cat walked by. The dog fought her natural instincts to chase the cat, seeing that the old man was so happy to have more help.

Old Man: Cat? Will you help us pull this turnip?

Old Woman: We have been pulling for a long time.

Girl: It won't come up.

Dog: It is stuck.

Cat: All right.

Old Man: I will pull the turnip.

Old Woman: I will pull the old man.

Girl: I will pull the old woman.

Dog: I will pull the little girl and you pull me.

Narrator: Again, they pulled the turnip. They pulled and pulled and pulled until beads of sweat popped out on their foreheads. The turnip was simply not going to move.

Turnip: I will show them.

Old Man: It won't move.

Old Woman: You are right.

Girl: We need more help.

Narrator: Along came a mouse. Of course, the cat couldn't help licking his lips. The mouse began to run away, for he had no wish to be eaten.

Old Man: Mouse? Will you help us pull this turnip?

Old Woman: We have been pulling for a long time.

Girl: It won't come up.

Dog: It is stuck.

Cat: If you help, I will try not to eat you.

Mouse: Well . . . .

Old Man: Please?

Mouse: All right.

Narrator: So they pulled and pulled and pulled until the turnip budged just a bit, and then they pulled some more. As stubborn as the turnip was, the old man, the old woman, the girl, the dog, the cat, and the mouse were even more stubborn and, of course, there were more of them.

Old Man: Pull!

Narrator: Well, the turnip finally popped out of the ground. Over toppled the old man, the old woman, the girl, the dog, the cat, and the mouse. The turnip landed on top.

Old Man: What an enormous turnip!

Old Woman: It is the biggest turnip I have ever seen!

Girl: Me, too!

Dog: Wow!

Cat: It's huge!

Mouse: No kidding!

Turnip: Put me back.

Old Man: What?!

Old Woman: It talks!

Turnip: Of course I can talk.

Old Man: Why didn't you talk to me before?

Turnip: Just when I thought you were my friend, you decided to pull me up and eat me.

Narrator: Well, the old man didn't know what to say in his own defense. The turnip, after all, was right.

Old Man: I will put you back.

Turnip: Thank you.

Narrator: And so he did. They patched up their differences and actually became quite good friends. They chatted with each other every evening. The old woman made them all some pumpkin pie. This pleased everyone much more than turnip pie ever would have—especially the turnip.

—The End—

The Ugly Duckling

The Ugly Duckling

Word List

a	end	must	then
am	fine	my	think
and	first	narrator	this
are	go	never	too
as	going	nice	ugly
ask	good	no	very
away	have	not	watch
babies	he	now	water
baby	hen	of	well
be	he's	on	what
before	him	one	whee
but	house	out	where
can	I	peep	who
cat	in	please	why
catch	is	quack	will
cluck	know	says	woman
come	lay	see	yes
course	let	sit	you
crack	let's	so	
do	little	squawk	
dog	look	stay	
don't	looking	swan	
duck	me	swim	
duckling	met	that	
egg	mice	that's	
eggs	mom	the	
	mother		

The Ugly Duckling

Characters

Narrator	Dog
Mother Duck	Woman
Little Duck	Swan
Ugly Duckling	
Hen	
Cat	

Suggested Props

eggs

Narrator: Once upon a time, near a lovely old farmhouse, there was a mother duck sitting upon her nest.

Mother Duck: Quack, quack.

Narrator: She peeked under and saw only two eggs.

Mother Duck: Quack!

Narrator: But that was all right with her. Two were better than none. She sat on the eggs until one day, one of them cracked open.

Mother Duck: Quack! My baby!

Little Duck: Peep, peep! Mom!

Narrator: Mother Duck thought her baby was the most beautiful in the world.

Mother Duck: Quack!

Narrator: She looked under again to see if her second egg had begun to crack.

Mother Duck: Quack! No crack!

Little Duck: No crack! Peep!

© Fearon Teacher Aids FE11001

Narrator:	So she sat some more. A ducky friend told her the egg was a dud and that she should tend to her duckling. But Mother Duck was determined to hatch her egg.
Mother Duck:	Quack! Come out, little duck!
Little Duck:	Come on, Mom! Let's swim!
Mother Duck:	Not now. I must sit on this egg.
Narrator:	At last, the egg cracked and the second chick emerged.
Ugly Duckling:	Squawk!
Narrator:	It was a very large, gray, funny-looking chick—not like the first fuzzy baby chick at all. Mother Duck knew she would love this ugly little duckling, too.
Mother Duck:	Quack! Let's swim!
Little Duck:	Quack! Me first!
Ugly Duckling:	Squawk! Me, too!
Narrator:	To everyone's surprise, the ugly little creature swam quite well. Mother Duck fluffed her tail feathers. She would show off her new family to the other farmyard animals.
Mother Duck:	Quack! See my babies?
Little Duck:	Quack!
Ugly Duckling:	Squawk!
Narrator:	Mother Duck became angry when the cows chuckled, the horses laughed, the sheep snickered, and the pigs poked fun. Mother Duck was far from amused.
Mother Duck:	Quack! Let him be!
Narrator:	The farm animals were rude enough to tell Mother Duck— right in front of the children—that her youngest duckling was quite ugly.

Mother Duck: He is not ugly. He is very nice. He can swim. He will be fine.

Narrator: And she swam off in a ducky huff. Of course, the ugly duckling felt perfectly awful. He wanted to hide. The other birds in the pond pecked at him and teased him until he could stand it no longer.

Ugly Duckling: I will go. Squawk!

Mother Duck: Quack! Please don't!

Little Duck: Quack! Stay!

Narrator: The ugly duckling packed his bags and left. He didn't go very far, though, just to the next farm, because he couldn't fly yet. There he met a hen in the yard.

Hen: Cluck! Who are you?

Ugly Duckling: Squawk! I am a duck.

Hen: You are?

Narrator: Hen had never met a duck quite like this one and, being a feather-brained bird, she believed him.

Ugly Duckling: Squawk! Can I stay?

Hen: I think so. I will ask the cat.

Narrator: A cat came out of the house.

Hen: Cat, can this duck stay?

Cat: Duck? That's not a duck.

Ugly Duckling: Of course I am a duck.

Cat: No, you are not.

Ugly Duckling: Then what am I?

Cat:	I do not know. I will ask the dog.

Narrator:	A dog came around the side of the house.

Cat:	Dog, can this duck stay?
Dog:	Duck? That's not a duck.
Ugly Duckling:	Of course I am a duck.
Dog:	No, you are not.
Ugly Duckling:	Then what am I?
Dog:	I do not know.

Narrator:	Now the poor ugly duckling was very confused. Who wouldn't be? The animals took the duck, or whatever he was, in the house to their mistress.

Woman:	What is this?
Hen:	He says he's a duck.
Cat:	He's not a duck.
Dog:	What is he?
Ugly Duckling:	Squawk!
Woman:	Can you lay eggs?
Ugly Duckling:	No.
Woman:	Can you catch mice?
Ugly Duckling:	No.
Woman:	Can you watch the house?
Ugly Duckling:	No, but I can swim.
Woman:	What good is that?

Narrator: The ugly duckling had no answer. He didn't feel good about anything he could do, like eat and waddle and swim. But the woman kept him on her farm and fed him. And the bird grew bigger and bigger until the woman could no longer keep him in her house. The ugly duckling made a mess of everything—he perched on her TV with his wings covering the screen, he sat in her favorite chair, and he pecked holes in her best curtains with his beak. So finally, she put him outside.

Ugly Duckling: Squawk! Now what?

Narrator: Indeed. Now what? The ugly duckling wandered down the road, feeling very alone. He came to a pond and jumped in for a little swim.

Ugly Duckling: Whee!

Narrator: And then he saw he was not alone at all. There swam the most beautiful bird he had ever seen, gliding upon the surface of the water. This beautiful bird had smooth white feathers and a long graceful neck.

Ugly Duckling: Who are you?

Swan: I am a swan.

Ugly Duckling: I have never met a swan before.

Narrator: To his dismay, the swan laughed at him. Hanging his head, he climbed out of the pond.

Swan: Where are you going?

Ugly Duckling: Away.

Swan: Why?

Ugly Duckling: I am so ugly.

Swan: Look in the water.

Narrator:	The ugly duckling looked in the water. Do you know what he saw? His reflection—and he saw that he looked just like the beautiful swan!

Ugly Duckling: What?!

Swan: You are a swan, too.

Ugly Duckling: I am?

Swan: Yes, and a very good-looking one as well.

Ugly Duckling: I am?

Swan: Yes.

Narrator:	Well, naturally, they fell in love, got married, and lived happily ever after. Now, can you imagine their surprise when, one day, Mother Swan looked under and spied a little purple egg? **—The End—**

The Shoemaker and the Elves

© Fearon Teacher Aids FE11001

The Shoemaker and the Elves

Word List

a	eat	know	really	to
am	elf	leather	rich	tonight
and	elves	let's	ripped	too
are	end	like	sack	two
at	enough	little	see	up
bags	ever	look	shirts	us
be	fast	made	shoemaker	watch
bread	fine	make	shoemaker's	we
bring	first	makes	shoes	wearing
but	food	me	sit	were
buy	for	money	some	what
can	four	more	someone	who
careful	get	my	soup	wife
clothes	gift	narrator	spaghetti	will
coats	going	noise	thank	with
come	good	of	that	work
course	have	oh	that's	wow
crackers	his	on	the	yes
dance	how	one	them	you
dear	hungry	pair	then	your
did	I	pairs	there	yum
didn't	idea	pants	these	
do	in	paper	they	
don't	is	pretty		
early	it	put		
	just			

The Shoemaker and the Elves

Characters

Narrator	Elf #1
Shoemaker	Elf #2
Shoemaker's Wife	Elf #3

Suggested Props

pieces of leather or cloth
table or bench
doll clothes
shoes
plate
bowl
bread
crackers

Narrator: There was once a shoemaker who was a very decent sort of fellow. He worked quite hard and never cheated anyone. But he did not earn enough money to feed himself and his wife properly.

Shoemaker: I am the shoemaker.

Shoemaker's Wife: I am his wife.

Shoemaker: Are you hungry?

Shoemaker's Wife: Yes.

Shoemaker: Me, too. What do we have to eat?

Shoemaker's Wife: Bread.

Shoemaker: Just bread?

Shoemaker's Wife: Yes.

Shoemaker: I have just enough leather to make one pair of shoes.

© Fearon Teacher Aids FE11001

Narrator:	The old man cut the leather and put it on his work bench, while his wife put the bread on the kitchen table.

Shoemaker: I will get up early to make the shoes.

**Shoemaker's
Wife:** Fine with me.

Narrator:	They ate their meager dinner. The wife left the bread on the table and they went to bed. Both of them were very sound sleepers.

**Shoemaker and
Shoemaker's
Wife:** Zzzzzzzz!

Narrator:	Meanwhile, three little elves crept into the shoe shop through an open window. They were cold, being dressed only in paper sacks, and they were hungry. But they were basically hard-working elves and wouldn't take food without doing some sort of work in return.

Elf #1: Look!

Elf #2: Leather!

Elf #3: We can make shoes!

Elf #1: First, we will eat.

Elf #2: There is some bread.

Elf #3: That will do.

Narrator:	They ate a bit of the bread. Then they sat down at the bench and made a beautiful pair of shoes from the leather.

Elf #1: What pretty shoes!

Narrator:	The elves gave each other high-fives and left through the window, being careful not to rip their flimsy paper clothes. The next morning, the shoemaker rose early to sew the leather into shoes.

Shoemaker: I am up. I will get to work.

Narrator: When he got to his bench, there were the shoes upon the worktable.

Shoemaker: Wife!

Shoemaker's Wife: What is it?

Shoemaker: Come look!

Shoemaker's Wife: Shoes! They are pretty. And you, my dear, are fast!

Shoemaker: But I didn't make them.

Shoemaker's Wife: Then who did?

Shoemaker: I don't know.

Narrator: Just then, a customer came into the shop. He was so pleased with the shoes that he paid the shoemaker twice their value.

Shoemaker: Wow!

Shoemaker's Wife: What will you buy?

Shoemaker: More leather for shoes, of course!

Narrator: And he did. The shoemaker bought enough leather for two pairs of shoes. When he got home, he was very hungry.

Shoemaker: Are you hungry?

Shoemaker's Wife: Yes.

Shoemaker: Me, too. What do we have to eat?

Shoemaker's Wife:	Soup and crackers.
Shoemaker:	Just soup and crackers?
Shoemaker's Wife:	Yes.
Shoemaker:	I have just enough leather to make two pairs of shoes.
Narrator:	The old man cut the leather and placed the pieces on his workbench. The wife put their dinner on the kitchen table.
Shoemaker:	I will get up early to make the shoes.
Shoemaker's Wife:	Fine with me.
Narrator:	After dinner, the wife, who was a bit forgetful, left the soup on the stove and the crackers on the table. Then they went up to bed.
Shoemaker and Shoemaker's Wife:	Zzzzzzzz!
Narrator:	Downstairs, the three little elves slipped into the shoemaker's house through the open window, just as they had the night before.
Elf #1:	Shh!
Elf #2:	Be careful!
Elf #3:	You ripped your sack!
Elf #1:	Look!
Elf #2:	Leather!
Elf #3:	We can make more shoes!

Elf #1:	First, we will eat.
Elf #2:	There is soup and crackers.
Elf #3:	That will do.
Narrator:	They ate some soup and a few crackers. Then they ran over to the bench and made two lovely pairs of shoes from the leather.
Elf #2:	Someone is really going to like these!
Narrator:	The three elves gave each other two high-fives, found some tape to repair their torn paper-sack clothing, and left through the window. The next morning, the old shoemaker awakened early. He meant to sew the leather into shoes.
Shoemaker:	I am up. I will get to work.
Narrator:	When he got to his workbench, two pairs of shoes were waiting for him.
Shoemaker:	Wife!
Shoemaker's Wife:	What is it?
Shoemaker:	Come look!
Shoemaker's Wife:	Shoes! They are pretty! And you, my dear, are fast!
Shoemaker:	But I didn't make them.
Shoemaker's Wife:	Then who did?
Shoemaker:	I don't know.
Narrator:	By noon that day, two customers had come in and bought the wonderful shoes. They were so happy with the shoes, they paid the shoemaker twice their worth.

© Fearon Teacher Aids FE11001

Shoemaker: Wow!

Shoemaker's Wife: What will you buy?

Shoemaker: More leather for shoes, of course!

Narrator: That is exactly what he did, too. He bought enough leather for four more pairs. By the time he got home, he was quite hungry.

Shoemaker: Are you hungry?

Shoemaker's Wife: Yes.

Shoemaker: Me, too. What do we have to eat?

Shoemaker's Wife: Spaghetti.

Shoemaker: Spaghetti? Yum!

Shoemaker's Wife: What do you have there?

Shoemaker: I have enough leather to make four pairs of shoes.

Narrator: And that is what occurred for many, many days. The shoemaker would buy the leather and cut it out for shoes, and overnight, the shoes would be finished. It wasn't long before the shoemaker and his wife weren't poor anymore.

Shoemaker: We have some money.

Shoemaker's Wife: Yes.

Shoemaker: Tonight we will sit up.

Shoemaker's Wife: Oh?

Shoemaker: We will watch to see who it is that makes the shoes.

Shoemaker's Wife: Good idea.

Narrator: So they hid themselves behind a curtain and pinched each other whenever they began to fall asleep. When the clock struck midnight, they heard an odd noise.

Shoemaker's Wife: What is that?

Shoemaker: Shh!

Narrator: The noise was a window creaking open. The shoemaker and his wife felt a cold draft blow across their feet. They peeked around the curtain.

Elf #1: Look!

Elf #2: Leather!

Elf #3: We can make shoes!

Elf #1: First, we will eat.

Elf #2: There is food there.

Elf #3: That food will do.

Narrator: The three elves ate and then sat at the bench to work. In no time, all the leather had been stitched into beautiful shoes.

Elf #3: These will bring in some money.

Narrator: Quick as a wink, the three elves gave each other high-fives and were off and away. The shoemaker and his wife came out from behind the curtain.

Shoemaker: Did you see that?

Shoemaker's Wife:	Elves!
Shoemaker:	They have made us rich.
Shoemaker's Wife:	How can we ever thank them?
Shoemaker:	Hmm . . . let's see . . . .
Shoemaker's Wife:	They were wearing paper bags.
Shoemaker:	That's it!
Shoemaker's Wife:	What?
Shoemaker:	We will make them some good clothes! I can make some little shoes.
Shoemaker's Wife:	I can make little pants and shirts and coats.
Shoemaker:	That will be a good gift.
Narrator:	And that is what they did. Instead of putting out shoe leather on the workbench that evening, they laid out the new clothes. Then they hid themselves behind the curtain to watch. The clock struck midnight.
Shoemaker's Wife:	What is that noise?
Shoemaker:	Shh!
Narrator:	A bit of snow blew in the open window as the elves climbed in.
Elf #1:	Look!
Elf #2:	Clothes!

Elf #3:	Let's put them on!

Narrator:	They tore off the ratty paper bags and put on the beautiful new clothes.

Elf #1:	Look at me!
Elf #2:	I look fine!
Elf #3:	Let's dance!

Narrator:	The shoemaker smiled at his wife and she smiled right back. The three little elves laughed and high-fived each other. They scampered out of the shop and into another fairy tale. And the old shoemaker and his wife never had to worry about money again. **—The End—**

Reproducible   **30**   © Fearon Teacher Aids FE11001

The Golden Goose

© Fearon Teacher Aids FE11001

Reproducible

The Golden Goose

Word List

a	end	I'm	now	the
all	farmer	in	of	then
am	farmer's	is	on	there
and	father	it	one	they
any	feather	it's	or	thirsty
are	for	juice	princess	to
boy	funny	king	problem	too
bread	get	land	right	want
brother	girl	laugh	said	water
can	give	little	sail	we
can't	go	loose	ship	welcome
cookie	going	make	some	well
cookies	golden	man	son	what
cracker	good	marry	still	what's
crackers	goose	me	stop	where
crouton	ha	milk	stuck	wife
cut	have	mine	sure	will
daughter	hello	mountain	surprise	wood
didn't	help	must	take	wow
dig	her	my	thank	yes
do	here	narrator	that	you
don't	him	no		
drink	hungry	not		
eat	I			
	if			

The Golden Goose

Characters

Narrator   Girl
Father   Farmer
Brother #1   Farmer's Wife
Little Man   Princess
Brother #2   King
Brother #3

Suggested Props

cookies, crackers, bread
thermos
stuffed bird
fake ax

Narrator:	Once, long ago, there was a man who had three sons. The two older boys were fairly smart, but not so nice. The third son, though kind, had been retained in second grade a couple of times. He just couldn't get that subtraction thing. Well, anyway, one cold day, the father realized they had no wood for cooking or warmth. He called his oldest boy.
Father:	We have no wood, my son.
Brother #1:	I will cut some, then.
Father:	Here are some cookies and milk for you.
Narrator:	The oldest son went into the forest, singing the latest hit song. Out of nowhere appeared a little man.
Little Man:	Hello.
Brother #1:	Hello.
Little Man:	Can I have a cookie?
Brother #1:	No. They are mine.
Little Man:	Can I have some milk, then?
Brother #1:	No. It's mine, too.

Narrator:	Well, the awful oldest brother rudely gobbled up his treats right in front of the little man. Of course, the little man was quite offended. In return for his rudeness, the little man cast a spell on the boy's ax so no trees could be cut for their fire.

Brother #1: What's going on?

Little Man: Ha, ha!

Narrator:	The boy went home with no firewood.

Father: Where is the wood?

Brother #1: I didn't get any.

Narrator:	Well, the father grounded the oldest son for two days and called for the middle son.

Father: We still have no wood, my son.

Brother #2: I will cut some, then.

Father: Here are some crackers and juice for you.

Narrator:	The second boy went into the forest, humming the latest commercial jingles. Out came the little man.

Little Man: Hello.

Brother #2: Hello.

Little Man: Can I have a cracker?

Brother #2: No. They are mine.

Little Man: Can I have some juice, then?

Brother #2: No. It's mine, too.

Narrator:	The second son also snarfed down the crackers and juice in two terrible mouthfuls. Was he rude or what? In return for his bad manners, the little man sent out his spell. When the boy tried to cut down the trees, his ax bounced right off the tree trunks.
Brother #2:	What's going on?
Little Man:	Ha, ha!
Narrator:	He, too, went home with no wood for the fire.
Father:	Where is the wood?
Brother #2:	I didn't get any.
Narrator:	The father put the boy in the time-out corner for four days. The father and his sons pulled their coats a little more tightly around their cold shoulders.
Brother #3:	I will go for the wood.
Father:	You?
Brother #3:	Yes. Me.
Father:	You can't do it.
Brother #3:	Yes, I can.
Father:	All right, then.
Narrator:	The father gave the youngest son some stale croutons and water. The boy skipped into the forest, reciting the alphabet.
Brother #3:	A, B, C, R, Z, L, T . . . .
Little Man:	Hello.
Brother #3:	Hello.
Little Man:	Can I have a crouton?

Brother #3: Sure.

Little Man: Can I have some water?

Brother #3: Sure.

Narrator: One thing the boy had learned well in his many years in second grade was how to share. And to his amazement, the stale croutons and water changed into apple turnovers and grape juice!

Brother #3: Wow!

Little Man: You are a good boy. I have a surprise for you.

Brother #3: What?

Little Man: Dig there.

Narrator: The little man pointed to an old, gnarled tree. When the boy dug down, he found a goose with golden feathers.

Brother #3: Thank you.

Little Man: You are welcome.

Narrator: The third son picked up the golden goose and began to walk home. Along the way, he met a girl sweeping a porch.

Girl: What do you have?

Brother #3: It is a golden goose.

Girl: I will take a feather.

Brother #3: No!

Narrator: But when the boy wasn't looking, she reached out for one, anyway.

Girl: I'm stuck! I can not get loose!

Narrator:	Indeed, she couldn't, for the little man of the forest had cast a spell on the goose. She was stuck.
Girl:	Help!
Narrator:	The boy continued on his way. He tucked the goose under his arm and the girl had no choice but to follow, for she was stuck. Soon, he met a farmer working in his fields.
Farmer:	What do you have?
Brother #3:	It is a golden goose.
Farmer:	I will take a feather.
Brother #3:	No!
Girl:	Don't!
Narrator:	But when the boy looked away, the farmer grabbed for a feather and he, too, was stuck.
Farmer:	Help! Help!
Narrator:	The farmer's wife heard his cries and came to rescue him. She was amazed to see the shiny golden goose with two people stuck to it.
Farmer's Wife:	What do you have?
Brother #3:	It is a golden goose.
Farmer's Wife:	I will take a feather.
Brother #3:	No!
Girl:	Don't!
Farmer:	Stop!

Narrator:	But she reached out despite their warnings, and she got stuck, too. The boy shook his head and led them down the dusty road. Eventually, they passed the castle of the kingdom. Now, in this castle lived a king who had a single daughter who was so sad that no one could make her laugh.
Brother #3:	I will make her laugh.
Narrator:	And that was exactly what happened. When the boy showed the princess the golden goose with everyone stuck to it, she laughed and laughed.
Princess:	Now, THAT is funny!
Narrator:	Now the king realized the princess would want to marry the boy with the golden goose. For some reason, he didn't like that idea. He thought of a plan to keep the boy from marrying his daughter.
King:	You must drink all the water in the well.
Brother #3:	I can not.
King:	You must if you want to marry my daughter.
Narrator:	The boy thought the little man of the forest might help. He found the little man sitting in the very spot where he had left him.
Brother #3:	I have a problem.
Little Man:	What is it?
Brother #3:	The king said I must drink all the water in the well.
Little Man:	Are you that thirsty?
Brother #3:	No.
Little Man:	Well, I am.
Brother #3:	You are?

Little Man:	Yes. Where is the well?

Narrator: The boy took the little man to the well. He drank and drank and, by dinnertime, the well was dry. The king was floored. He thought of another plan.

King: You must eat a mountain of bread.

Brother #3: I can not.

King: You must if you want to marry my daughter.

Narrator: The boy hoped the little forest man could help. Guess where he found the man? Just where he'd been before!

Brother #3: I have a problem.

Little Man: What is it?

Brother #3: The king said I must eat a mountain of bread.

Little Man: Are you that hungry?

Brother #3: No.

Little Man: Well, I am.

Brother #3: You are?

Little Man: Yes. Where is the mountain?

Narrator: The boy took him to the mountain of bread. The little man began eating and, by evening, every scrap was gone. You would think the king would give up, but he tried a third time.

King: You must give me a ship that can sail on land or on water.

Brother #3: I can not.

King: You must if you want to marry my daughter.

Narrator:	The boy felt as if he'd finally been tricked. But he went to see the little man of the forest for advice.

Brother #3:   I have a problem.

Little Man: What is it?

Brother #3:   The king said I must give him a ship that can sail on land or on water.

Little Man: Can you give him one?

Brother #3:   No.

Little Man: Well, I can.

Brother #3:   You can?

Little Man: Yes.

Narrator:	And so he did. When the king saw the wonderful ship, he knew he had been beaten by the boy who couldn't pass second grade. The boy and the king's daughter were married. The little man of the forest was best man and the golden goose was the flower girl. And everyone lived happily ever after—except, of course, for the three people stuck to the magical golden goose. **—The End—**

Rapunzel

Rapunzel

Word List

a	find	more	sprouts	will
again	fine	my	stealing	witch
always	get	narrator	thank	woman
am	give	never	that	yes
and	go	no	the	you
are	guess	not	them	your
beat	ha	now	there	
because	hair	oh	these	
brussels	happy	okay	those	
call	have	one	up	
can	hello	ouch	want	
checkers	help	out	wanted	
child	here	play	we	
climb	how	please	what	
climbs	husband	police	where	
come	I	pretty	who	
dare	if	prince	why	
do	is	promise	wife	
don't	it	Rapunzel		
down	leave	really		
end	let	some		
fast	let's			
	made			
	me			

Rapunzel

Characters	Suggested Props
Narrator	bucket
Woman	green balls (brussels sprouts)
Husband	thick rope (braid)
Witch	broom
Rapunzel	cactus
Prince	scissors
	checkers game

Narrator: Once upon a time, a woman and her husband lived in a dark forest near a powerful witch.

Woman: I am the woman.

Husband: I am the husband.

Witch: And I am the witch! Ha!

Narrator: More than anything, the woman and her husband wanted a child. One day, instead of wishing for a child, the woman wished for some lovely brussels sprouts.

Woman: I want some brussels sprouts.

Husband: Brussels sprouts?

Woman: Yes.

Husband: Where will I get brussels sprouts?

Narrator: The woman pointed to the powerful witch's garden.

Husband: You want those brussels sprouts?

Woman: Yes.

Narrator: Now, the man loved his wife very much, and even though he knew it was wrong to trespass and steal, he climbed over the fence and filled a bucket with the lovely green brussels sprouts.

Husband: Here are your brussels sprouts.

Woman: Thank you!

Narrator: She gobbled them up—every last one. Unfortunately, the next day, she wanted more brussels sprouts.

Woman: I want more brussels sprouts.

Husband: No, you don't.

Woman: Yes, I do.

Husband: Where will I get more brussels sprouts?

Narrator: The woman pointed to the powerful witch's garden.

Husband: Those?

Woman: Yes.

Narrator: So over the fence he went again, stealing a bucketful of brussels sprouts.

Husband: Are you happy now?

Woman: Yes.

Narrator: And she was . . . for a while.

Woman: I want more brussels sprouts.

Husband: No, you don't.

Woman: Yes, I do.

Husband: Where will I get these brussels sprouts?

Narrator: Of course, she pointed to the witch's lovely garden.

Husband: Those?

Woman: Yes.

Narrator:	This time, however, just as the husband was climbing over the fence with a full bucket of luscious, green brussels sprouts, something snagged his pants leg.

Husband: What is that?

Witch: It is I, the witch!

Husband: Help!

Witch: You are stealing my brussels sprouts!

Husband: Yes, I guess I am.

Narrator:	How could he deny it, with the bucket of sprouts there in his hand? Now the clever witch also wanted something and she saw a way to get it. So instead of calling the forest police, she decided to trick the man.

Witch: How dare you!

Husband: My wife wanted them.

Witch: I will call the police.

Husband: Please don't.

Narrator:	Well, it took a lot of convincing, but the husband finally got the witch to let him go and not call the forest police. Unfortunately, he made a rather bad bargain.

Witch: I will let you go if you give me your child.

Husband: I don't have one.

Witch: You will.

Husband: Okay.

Narrator:	Too bad for the husband. Soon a child was born to the husband and his wife. The witch soon appeared at their door to take the child away.

Witch: Give me the child!

Woman: No!

Husband: Please don't!

Witch: You made a promise.

Narrator: The husband knew she was right, and because he didn't want her to call the police, he gave her the baby. The witch named the beautiful baby Rapunzel, and in spite of what you know about witches, she loved her very much. Rapunzel grew up, and soon the witch realized she couldn't keep the girl much longer, so she shut her in a tower in the middle of the forest. The tower had no steps, no door, and only one window. When the witch wanted to visit, she would stand below the window and call up to the girl.

Witch: Rapunzel, Rapunzel! Let down your hair!

Rapunzel: Okay.

Narrator: Rapunzel had amazingly long, luxurious hair, and when she heard the witch call out, she dropped her long hair down to the ground and the witch would slowly climb up.

Witch: How are you?

Rapunzel: I am fine.

Narrator: Living in a tower can be very lonesome, so Rapunzel was always happy to see the witch. She sang songs for the witch. They played checkers. They sewed lovely things to make the tower a more beautiful home.

Rapunzel: Can we go out?

Witch: No.

Rapunzel: Why not?

Witch: Because.

Narrator: The witch never gave Rapunzel a really good reason for keeping her locked away. We can only guess it was because Rapunzel was the only person the witch could beat at checkers.

Witch: Let's play checkers.

Rapunzel: No. You always beat me.

© Fearon Teacher Aids FE11001

Witch:	Ha!

Narrator: Well, one day, when the witch was out having her hair undone, a dashing prince came riding by the tower. He stopped to listen to Rapunzel sing.

Rapunzel: Tra la la!

Prince: That is pretty!

Narrator: The prince tried to find a way into the tower, but, of course, there was only one way. Being a curious fellow, he came back the next day. He hid behind a tree and waited. And there he saw the witch.

Witch: Rapunzel, Rapunzel! Let down your hair!

Rapunzel: Okay.

Narrator: So now the prince saw how to get up into the tower.

Witch: Let's play checkers.

Rapunzel: No. You always beat me.

Witch: Ha!

Narrator: The next day, the prince rode out to the tower.

Prince: Rapunzel, Rapunzel! Let down your hair!

Rapunzel: Okay.

Narrator: To his surprise, down came the long hair. Being an athletic sort of guy, he climbed right up.

Prince: Hello!

Rapunzel: Eeek! Who are you?

Prince: I am the prince.

Rapunzel: Oh. Do you play checkers?

| Narrator: | Much to her delight, the prince was terrible at checkers and Rapunzel was able to win all the games. |

Prince: Can I come again?

Rapunzel: Yes.

| Narrator: | All was well, until one day Rapunzel accidentally told the secret. |

Witch: Rapunzel, Rapunzel! Let down your hair!

Rapunzel: Okay.

Witch: What a climb!

Rapunzel: The prince climbs up fast!

Witch: Who?

Rapunzel: The prince.

| Narrator: | The witch became so angry she grabbed up a pair of scissors and snipped off Rapunzel's long, luxurious hair. Then she took Rapunzel from the tower on her broomstick and put her in a desert. |

Witch: There!

Rapunzel: Don't leave me here!

| Narrator: | She DID leave Rapunzel, and flew back to the tower. |

Witch: I will get the prince.

Prince: Rapunzel, Rapunzel! Let down your hair!

Witch: Here.

| Narrator: | The witch tossed the braid out the window, and up climbed the prince. You can imagine his surprise when, instead of Rapunzel, the girl of his dreams, there stood the old nasty witch. |

Prince: Who are you?

Witch: I am the witch!

Narrator:	And she pushed him right out the window.
Prince:	Help!
Narrator:	He landed on a cactus, which probably hurt like all get out. The little cactus needles went everywhere.
Prince:	Ouch!
Witch:	Now you will never find Rapunzel!
Narrator:	The prince wandered for a year looking for someone who could pick out all the cactus stickers. One day, he just happened to stagger into the desert where Rapunzel had been taken by the witch.
Prince:	Help!
Rapunzel:	Who is there?
Prince:	It is the prince.
Rapunzel:	Really?
Narrator:	They were so happy to see one another that they cried tears of joy. Rapunzel picked out the cactus needles, and when the task was done, they decided to get married and return to the prince's castle to live. The witch was so angry, she ate too many brussels sprouts and exploded. And that was the end of her.

—The End—

The Princess and the Pea

The Princess and the Pea

Word List

a	girl	not	something	weed
all	grow	of	son	welcome
am	hard	oh	soon	we'll
and	have	ouch	still	wet
are	help	out	stop	what
as	here	own	talking	when
badly	here's	pea	thank	where
be	hid	peas	that	who
bed	how	pick	that's	who's
but	I	plant	the	why
can	in	prince	them	wife
cold	is	princess	then	will
come	it	queen	there	wish
cool	joking	real	to	with
could	just	right	under	yes
course	kingdom	rock	very	you
did	leave	said	want	your
do	make	say	wants	you're
end	mattress	see	was	
find	me	she		
food	mother	sleep		
from	my	some		
garden	narrator			
get	need			
	no			

The Princess and the Pea

Characters	Suggested Props
Narrator	pea
Prince	bed
Queen	plant
Pea	
Princess	

Narrator: Once upon a time, in a magical land far away, there was a prince who wanted to have his own kingdom. In his dream kingdom, the prince wanted to grow his favorite vegetable—peas.

Prince: I want my own kingdom. I will grow peas.

Queen: You are joking.

Prince: No. I am not.

Narrator: Now, in order to have his very own kingdom of peas, the prince knew he needed someone to help him.

Prince: I need a wife.

Queen: She will have to be a real princess.

Prince: Of course.

Narrator: So the prince traveled all over the world to find a princess who would help him with his kingdom of peas. He always asked the same questions.

Prince: Will you be my princess?

Narrator: Naturally, all the girls agreed to this question. But then, the prince would ask the most important questions.

52

© Fearon Teacher Aids FE11001

Prince: Will you plant peas with me? Will you help weed the garden? Will you pick peas?

Narrator: And the beautiful ladies all said the same thing: NO! Sadly, the prince went back home without a wife.

Prince: I still want my own kingdom. I want to grow peas.

Narrator: The queen, his mother, felt sorry for him and bought him a magical pea plant.

Queen: Here, my son.

Prince: Thank you, Mother!

Narrator: He took the pea plant to its very own room. There, he discovered an amazing secret—the plant could talk!

Prince: I wish I could find a princess.

Pea: You will.

Prince: What? Who said that?

Pea: I did.

Narrator: Well, naturally, the prince was floored!

Prince: But I want my own kingdom, and I want to grow peas.

Pea: That's cool.

Prince: But no princess wants to help me plant, weed, and pick them.

Pea: She will find you.

Prince: She will? When?

Pea: Soon.

Narrator:	The prince didn't have to wait long. One evening, while showing his mother how large Pea had grown, a terrible storm began. The rain poured down as if dumped from a giant's pitcher. The lightning lit up the sky. And the thunder—it was enough to make even Pea hide under the bed!

Queen: Where is Pea?

Prince: It hid under the bed.

Pea: Make it stop!

Queen: You are joking.

Prince: No, I am not.

Narrator:	They tried and tried, but they could not make the pea plant come out from under the bed.

Pea: Make it stop!

Narrator:	In spite of the thunder, they heard a knock at the door.

Queen: I will see who it is.

Prince: I will get Pea out from under the bed.

Queen: Just leave it.

Pea: Make it stop!

Narrator:	The prince ran down to the kitchen to get the frightened pea plant a cold drink of water. While he was gone, the pea plant ran into another room. Meanwhile, the queen pulled the door open. There stood a girl.

Princess: I am a princess.

Queen: Oh?

Princess: I am wet and cold. Can I come in?

Queen: All right.

Narrator:	The queen let the girl in, against her better judgment.

 © Fearon Teacher Aids FE11001

Princess: Thank you.

Queen: You're welcome.

Narrator: The girl who said she was a princess looked like something the pond had spit out. Her hair dripped water. Her clothes were soaking wet. Water ran out of her shoes.

Queen: You're a princess?

Princess: Of course.

Queen: We'll see.

Narrator: The queen thought of a thousand questions to ask the poor, wet girl. Finally, she took her to a room, and while the princess was getting ready for bed, she happened to see the pea plant hiding in the corner.

Queen: Psst. Come here.

Pea: Why?

Queen: I need you.

Pea: You do?

Narrator: The queen picked a pea off the pea plant.

Pea: Ouch!

Queen: Shh!

Narrator: Then the queen quickly put a single pea under 20 feather mattresses before the girl could see what she was doing.

Queen: Here's your bed.

Princess: Thank you.

Narrator: And the tired girl climbed into bed. The queen left, pulling the door shut behind her. The pea plant was locked in with the girl.

Pea: Psst. Girl.

Princess: Who's that?

Pea: Me, the pea plant.

Princess: A talking pea plant?

Pea: Yes.

Narrator: Naturally, the princess was surprised.

Pea: Do you want to be queen?

Princess: Yes.

Pea: Then you have to do as I say.

Princess: All right.

Narrator: Pea, who loved to talk, kept the poor girl up all night, so she looked simply awful when the queen brought in her breakfast the next morning.

Queen: Here is some food.

Princess: Thank you.

Queen: How did you sleep?

Princess: Very badly.

Queen: Oh?

Princess: There was something as hard as a rock under my mattress. I could not sleep.

Narrator: The queen was delighted to hear the news, for only a real princess could feel something as tiny as a pea under 20 feather mattresses. She ran to find the prince and tell him the good news.

Prince: Thank you, Pea.

Pea: You are welcome.

56 © Fearon Teacher Aids FE11001

Prince: Will you be my princess?

Princess: Yes.

Prince: Will you plant peas with me?

Princess: Yes.

Prince: Will you help weed the garden?

Princess: Yes.

Prince: Will you pick peas?

Princess: Yes.

Narrator: And so the prince married the princess. Pea looked smashing in his best man's tuxedo at the wedding. Pea gave the princess a pea-plant wink, knowing that anyone who was willing to stay up all night listening to his stories had to be all right. And they all lived happily ever after, especially the pea plant, who never got plucked again.

—The End—

Rumpelstiltskin

© Fearon Teacher Aids FE11001

Rumpelstiltskin

Word List

am	have	not	thank
be	hello	okay	that
but	help	or	the
by	I	problem	this
can	if	promise	three
cannot	into	promised	to
Caspar	is	ribs	told
child	it	ring	try
daughter	Jack	roast	want
days	Joe	Rumpelstiltskin	what
egg	king	see	who
end	marry	shanks	will
first	me	she	work
get	miller	sheep	yes
give	miller's	something	you
gold	morning	sorry	you'll
goose	must	spin	your
guess	my	straw	
ha	name	Teddy	
Harry	narrator		
	necklace		
	no		

Rumpelstiltskin

Characters	Suggested Props
Narrator	crown
Miller	baby doll
Miller's Daughter	straw
King	necklace
Rumpelstiltskin	gold coins
	ring

Narrator: There once was a miller who was very poor.

Miller: I am the miller.

Narrator: He had a very wonderful daughter.

Miller's Daughter: I am the miller's daughter.

Narrator: One day, the king rode by the mill. Heaven only knows what possessed the miller, but he told a whopping big lie to the king.

Miller: My daughter can spin straw into gold.

King: She can?

Miller's Daughter: I can?

Narrator: The king told the miller to bring the girl to the castle the very next day. You can imagine how she felt.

Miller's Daughter: I cannot spin straw into gold.

Miller: You can try.

© Fearon Teacher Aids FE11001

Narrator:	Well, the king put her in a room filled with straw. He gave her a spinning wheel.
King:	Get to work. I want to see gold by morning or you'll be sorry.
Narrator:	The girl was stunned. She could no more spin straw into gold than you could. She began to cry.
Miller's Daughter:	Boo hoo!
Narrator:	Suddenly, the door opened and in came a funny little man.
Rumpelstiltskin:	Hello.
Miller's Daughter:	Hello.
Rumpelstiltskin:	What is it?
Miller's Daughter:	I have to spin this straw into gold.
Rumpelstiltskin:	I can help you.
Miller's Daughter:	You can?
Rumpelstiltskin:	Yes, but you must give me something.
Miller's Daughter:	What?
Rumpelstiltskin:	Your necklace.
Narrator:	To the girl, it seemed to be a very good deal. She agreed at once and the man set to work. By morning, the room was filled with gold.
Miller's Daughter:	Thank you!

Rumpelstiltskin: No problem.

Narrator: However, there WAS a problem. The king was so pleased with all the gold that he led the poor girl to a bigger room filled with straw.

King: Get to work. I want to see gold by morning or you'll be sorry.

Narrator: The girl knew she was in big trouble. Even though she'd watched the funny little man work all night, she still couldn't spin straw into gold. She started to cry.

Miller's Daughter: Boo hoo!

Narrator: The door swung open and there stood the little man.

Rumpelstiltskin: Hello.

Miller's Daughter: Hello.

Rumpelstiltskin: What is it?

Miller's Daughter: I have to spin this straw into gold.

Rumpelstiltskin: I will help you.

Miller's Daughter: You will?

Rumpelstiltskin: Yes, but you must give me something.

Miller's Daughter: What?

Rumpelstiltskin: Your ring.

Narrator: This was also a good deal. She agreed to it at once. The man set to work and by morning, the second room was piled high with shining gold coins.

Miller's Daughter: Thank you!

Rumpelstiltskin: No problem.

Narrator: Well, it really was a problem, because the greedy king took the miller's daughter to a third, even larger room. It was filled with straw.

King: Get to work. I want to see gold by morning or you'll be sorry.

Narrator: She was already sorry. No sooner had the girl begun to wind up for a really good cry when the little man popped in.

Rumpelstiltskin: Hello.

Miller's Daughter: Hello.

Rumpelstiltskin: What is it?

Miller's Daughter: I have to spin this straw into gold.

Rumpelstiltskin: I will help you.

Miller's Daughter: You will?

Rumpelstiltskin: Yes, but you must give me something.

Miller's Daughter: What?

Narrator: This time, the little man saw that, indeed, she had nothing to give. He sat on a bale of hay and thought very hard.

Rumpelstiltskin: You must give me your first child.

Miller's Daughter: I have no child.

Rumpelstiltskin: Promise.

Miller's Daughter: Okay.

Narrator: So the little man went to work and by daylight, the room was filled with gold. The king was so pleased he decided to marry the miller's daughter at once.

King: Marry me.

Miller's Daughter: Okay.

Narrator: Well, in a year or so, they had a child and to the new queen's dismay, the funny little man came back.

Rumpelstiltskin: Give me the child.

Miller's Daughter: No!

Rumpelstiltskin: You promised.

Miller's Daughter: I will give you gold.

Rumpelstiltskin: Ha! I can spin straw into gold.
I want the child.

Narrator: The miller's daughter cried so hard she almost washed the little man right out of the castle. The thought of being drowned in a flood of tears made the little man decide to give her another chance.

Rumpelstiltskin: You have three days to guess my name.

Miller's Daughter: Three days?

Rumpelstiltskin: Yes. If you cannot, I get the child.

Narrator:	She stayed up the whole night thinking of names. She even sent a messenger to ask for all the most unusual names in the kingdom. The next day, the little man was back.

Rumpelstiltskin: What is my name?

Miller's Daughter: Joe?

Rumpelstiltskin: No. That is not my name.

Miller's Daughter: Caspar?

Rumpelstiltskin: No. That is not my name.

Miller's Daughter: Teddy?

Rumpelstiltskin: No. That is not my name.

Narrator:	The second day, she guessed more very unusual names.

Rumpelstiltskin: What is my name?

Miller's Daughter: Roast ribs?

Rumpelstiltskin: No. That is not my name.

Miller's Daughter: Goose egg?

Rumpelstiltskin: No. That is not my name.

Miller's Daughter: Sheep shanks?

Rumpelstiltskin: No. That is not my name.

Narrator:	On the third day, the messenger returned and whispered a very strange message in the queen's ear. She smiled as the funny little man came in.

Rumpelstiltskin: What is my name?

Miller's Daughter: Harry?

Rumpelstiltskin: No. That is not my name.

Miller's Daughter: Jack?

Rumpelstiltskin: No. That is not my name.

Miller's Daughter: Is it Rumpelstiltskin?

Rumpelstiltskin: Who told you that?!?!

Narrator: The funny little man became so angry that when he stamped his foot, a crack opened up in the earth that swallowed him right up. And as far as we know, he was never heard from again. The moral of this story, of course, is to never ask strangers to spin straw into gold for you without first making proper introductions.

—The End—

The Emperor's New Suit

The Emperor's New Suit

Word List

a	fit	lot	pretty	thief
am	for	lots	put	think
and	good	love	quite	this
are	governor	make	red	too
aren't	grand	march	saw	underwear
at	great	mayor	say	very
be	ha	me	see	we
boy	has	money	seen	welcome
by	hat	more	should	well
cannot	have	must	some	what
check	he	my	special	where
clever	hear	narrator	stupid	who
cloth	here	new	suit	will
clothes	his	no	tell	work
coat	how	not	thank	yes
coming	I	of	the	you
cost	if	oh	them	you're
course	in	on	then	
do	invisible	or	they	
done	is	pants		
emperor	isn't	parade		
emperor's	it	people		
end	know			
	like			
	look			

The Emperor's New Suit

Characters

Narrator Governor
Emperor   Mayor
Thief #1   Boy
Thief #2
Thief #3

Suggested Props

knitting needles
scissors
crown
red long johns
bucket

Narrator: Long, long ago, there lived an emperor who spent every gold coin he had on clothes. It didn't matter that the royal soldiers wore rags or that the city streets were full of holes. He just had to have new clothes.

Emperor: More clothes!

Narrator: One day, three clever thieves came to the royal city.

Thief #1: I am a thief.

Thief #2: Me, too!

Thief #3: We are very clever!

Narrator: When they heard of the emperor's passion for clothes, they rubbed their hands together with glee and hatched a plan.

Thief #1: We will make clothes for the emperor.

Thief #2: The clothes will be pretty and cost a lot.

Thief #3: The clothes will be invisible!

All Thieves: Ha, ha, ha!

Thief #1: We will say the clothes cannot be seen by people who are no good.

Thief #2:   We will say the clothes cannot be seen by people who are stupid.

Thief #3:   We are clever!

All Thieves: Ha, ha, ha!

Narrator: So they set up a shop, knowing the emperor couldn't resist any new and wonderful clothes. And sure enough, the emperor and his two best friends, the governor and the mayor, saw the clothes shop and peeked in.

Emperor: Cloth! I must have some!

Governor: I hear it is special cloth.

Mayor: The cloth cannot be seen by people who are no good or stupid.

Emperor: I must have a new suit of this cloth! Then I will know who is no good or stupid.

Narrator: And the emperor sent a bucket of gold coins to the three thieves so they could begin on his new suit.

All Thieves: Ha, ha, ha!

Narrator: They sat at the empty looms day and night, eating good food and doing no work at all. The emperor finally became curious about how his new suit was coming along.

Emperor: Where is my new suit?

Governor: I will check.

Narrator: So the governor went to the shop to check on the cloth. Of course, he found the three thieves hard at work on the invisible cloth.

Thief #1:   Do you like it?

Governor: Oh, yes.

Thief #2:   Isn't it pretty?

Governor: Yes.

Thief #3: Will the emperor like it?

Narrator: The governor didn't really know what to say. So he quickly left the shop. Once outside, he scratched his head and thought right out loud.

Governor: I see no cloth. What should I tell the emperor? He will think I am no good or stupid if I say I saw no cloth.

Narrator: The three thieves were peeking out the window, listening to the governor. They had a really good laugh at his confusion.

All Thieves: Ha, ha, ha!

Narrator: The governor went back to the emperor with his report on the new suit.

Emperor: Well?

Governor: It is very pretty.

Emperor: It is?

Governor: Er . . . yes.

Emperor: Is it done?

Governor: No. Not quite.

Narrator: The emperor foolishly sent more money—a whole wheelbarrow full, as a matter of fact.

Thief #1: This is great!

Thief #2: Lots of money!

Thief #3: And no work!

All Thieves: Ha, ha, ha!

Narrator:	And they continued to sit in front of the empty looms, pretending to work. Soon, the emperor grew impatient. He sent his friend, the mayor, to check on the cloth.
Thief #1:	Do you like it?
Mayor:	Oh, yes.
Thief #2:	Isn't it pretty?
Mayor:	Yes.
Thief #3:	Will the emperor like it?
Narrator:	The mayor couldn't answer because he didn't want to seem no good and stupid. So he ran out of the shop. He worried about what to tell the emperor.
Mayor:	I see no cloth. What should I tell the emperor? He will think I am no good or stupid if I say I saw no cloth.
Narrator:	The thieves were listening to the mayor's little speech. They hid their laughter behind their hands until the poor man left. Then they could hold it in no more.
Thief #1:	This is great!
Thief #2:	Lots of money!
Thief #3:	And no work!
All Thieves:	Ha, ha, ha!
Narrator:	The mayor dragged his heels all the way back. He dreaded giving the report.
Emperor:	Well?
Mayor:	It is very pretty.
Emperor:	Is it?
Mayor:	Er . . . yes.
Emperor:	Is it done?

© Fearon Teacher Aids FE11001

Mayor:	No. Not quite.
Narrator:	The governor glanced at the mayor and they shrugged.
Emperor:	I must see it!
Governor and Mayor:	What?!?!
Emperor:	I must see the cloth!
Narrator:	The governor and the mayor gulped, but there was no stopping the emperor. Off they marched, right into the thieves' shop. Luckily, the thieves had stopped laughing. They were hard at work, pretending to weave the special cloth.
Thief #1:	Look at the cloth!
Thief #2:	Isn't it pretty?
Thief #3:	Do you like it?
Narrator:	The emperor was speechless. He saw absolutely nothing on the loom. But he didn't want to seem foolish or unfit to be emperor.
Emperor:	It is pretty. I love it!
Narrator:	That made the thieves very happy, for they knew their trick was working. Quickly, they stood up, holding invisible garments in their fingers.
Thief #1:	See the coat!
Thief #2:	See the pants!
Thief #3:	See the hat!
Thief #1:	Aren't they pretty?
Thief #2:	Do you like them?
Thief #3:	They will fit!

Boy: A parade!

Thief #1: What?

Boy: A parade is coming!

Thief #2: You must march, Emperor!

Emperor: What?

Thief #3: You must be in the parade!

Emperor: Of course.

Thief #1: Here. Put on the coat.

Thief #2: Here. Put on the pants.

Thief #3: Here. Put on the hat.

Narrator: Guess what? The emperor pulled off his royal pants, royal coat, and royal hat. There he stood in his long red underwear, which, I might add, he wisely left on.

Thief #1: Here is the coat.

Thief #2: Here are the pants.

Thief #3: Here is the hat.

Emperor: Thank you.

All Thieves: You're welcome.

Emperor: How do I look?

Governor and Mayor: Great!

Narrator: They hurried outside to join the parade. The governor and the mayor pretended to be very impressed with the emperor's new suit, because, of course, they didn't wish to seem no good or stupid.

Governor: Isn't the emperor grand?

Mayor: Aren't his clothes great?

Narrator: The crowd nodded and clapped. Several people, who hadn't heard of the trick, just looked confused. And then it happened.

Boy: He has no clothes!

Governor and Mayor: What?

Boy: The emperor is in his underwear! Look!

Narrator: The gentlemen in the crowd blushed. The ladies in the crowd covered their eyes. And the children in the crowd giggled and pointed their fingers at the emperor.

Boy: Look! The emperor has on red underwear!

Narrator: Everyone began to laugh. The emperor tried to ignore his subjects as he walked the length of the parade in his long red underwear—all the way back to the palace. The three thieves took advantage of the situation by packing up all the gold the emperor had given them and quickly leaving town. The next day, the emperor fired the governor and the mayor for laughing at his red underwear. He immediately switched to white underwear, and he never bought any more clothes without first checking with his wife.

—The End—

The Frog Prince

© Fearon Teacher Aids FE11001

The Frog Prince

Word List

a	eat	is	play	thirsty
all	end	it	please	tired
am	find	jewels	prince	to
and	first	keep	princess	too
are	for	kind	promise	up
at	found	king	promised	wait
ball	friend	kiss	queen	want
be	frog	let	right	was
but	from	let's	said	what
can	get	lift	saw	who
carry	giant	lost	see	who's
could	give	made	share	why
crown	golden	me	sit	will
crying	good	must	sleep	with
cup	have	my	smart	won't
cute	he	narrator	so	wonderful
deal	help	no	something	yes
did	here	of	table	you
dinner	him	on	thank	your
do	his	oops	the	yuck
does	how	open	then	
door	I	pillow	there	
drink	if	plate		
	in			

The Frog Prince

Characters
Narrator
King
Queen
Princess
Frog

Suggested Props
ball
table
plate
cup
pillow

Narrator: Long ago, there lived a king and a queen who had a very smart and wonderful daughter.

King: I am the king.

Queen: I am the queen.

Princess: And I am the smart and wonderful princess.

Narrator: Their castle lay close to a forest. Each day, the princess went into this forest to play with her golden ball, because, of course, in those days they had no television to watch.

Princess: I will play with my ball.

Narrator: She spent a lot of time just tossing the ball up and catching it. Well, one day, she missed and the ball went right into a pond.

Princess: Oops!

Narrator: Down it went, right into the murky bottom. She did what most people do when they've just lost their favorite toy.

Princess: Boo hoo! I lost my ball!

Narrator: Suddenly, she heard a strange voice.

Frog: What is it?

Narrator:	The princess looked up. It was a big, green frog.
Princess:	Yuck! A frog!
Narrator:	Wasn't that rude of her?
Frog:	Why are you crying?
Princess:	I lost my ball.
Frog:	I can help.
Narrator:	Now, being a princess, she was used to certain advantages, one of which was having people wait on her hand and foot. She'd never had a frog serve her before, but she knew an opportunity when it arose.
Princess:	How can you help?
Frog:	I will get your ball.
Princess:	Good. Thank you.
Frog:	But you must give me something, too.
Princess:	All right. Do you want my golden crown?
Frog:	No.
Princess:	Do you want my jewels?
Frog:	No.
Princess:	What do you want?
Narrator:	The frog wrinkled his brow in thought and finally croaked out an answer.
Frog:	I want to be your friend.
Princess:	My friend?
Frog:	Yes. I want to sit at your table.
Princess:	Sit at my table?!

Frog: I want to eat from your plate.

Princess: Eat from my plate?!?!

Frog: I want to drink from your cup.

Princess: Drink from my cup?!?!?!

Frog: I want to sleep on your pillow.

Princess: What? Yuck!

Frog: Is it a deal?

Princess: No!

Frog: All right. I won't get your ball.

Narrator: The frog began to hop back into the pond. The princess decided she could make a few sacrifices to get her golden ball back.

Princess: Frog?

Frog: Yes.

Princess: I will do what you want.

Frog: Good. I will get your ball.

Narrator: Well, the frog dove deep into the muddy pond, and, true to his word, brought up the ball.

Frog: Here.

Princess: Thank you!

Narrator: Now, being an only child, the princess was a bit self-centered, and she snatched up the ball and ran back to the castle, forgetting her promise to the frog.

Frog: Wait for me!

King:	Who is it?
Queen:	Who's there?
Frog:	Let me in.
King:	Princess, open the door.
Queen:	Yes, let's see who it is.

| **Narrator:** | You can imagine her surprise when the princess saw the frog! |

| **Princess:** | You! |
| **Frog:** | Yes! |

| **Narrator:** | She slammed the door in his froggy little face. |

King:	Who was it?
Queen:	A giant?
Princess:	No.
King:	Who, then?
Princess:	A frog.
Queen:	What does he want?
Princess:	I said he could be my friend if he found my lost ball.
King:	Did he find it?
Princess:	Yes.
Queen:	So you must be his friend.
King:	Are you?

Princess: No.

Narrator: Well, her parents threw an absolute fit at that answer. It was unthinkable that a royal princess who was so wonderful and smart would go back on her word. The king and the queen pitched a royal tantrum and, to make a messy family fit shorter, the fight left the princess in tears for the second time that day.

King: You made a promise.

Queen: You must keep it.

Princess: All right.

Narrator: So, in hopped the happy frog, right up to the dinner table.

Frog: Lift me up, please.

Princess: What?!

Frog: You promised.

King: Did you promise?

Princess: Yes.

Queen: Lift him up, then.

Narrator: Now the frog was on the table.

Frog: Share your dinner, please.

Princess: What?!

Frog: You promised.

King: Did you promise?

Princess: Yes.

Queen: Share your dinner with him, then.

Frog: I am thirsty.

Princess: What?!

Frog: You promised.

King: Did you promise?

Princess: Yes.

Queen: Let him drink, then.

Narrator: Can you imagine how the princess felt? A gross, green, rather dry frog not only takes command of her home, but eats from her plate AND puts his froggy lips on her cup! She was disgusted, to say the least. And the whole affair had quite spoiled her own appetite. But the worst was yet to come. The frog yawned.

Frog: I am tired.

Princess: What?!

Frog: Carry me to your pillow, please.

Princess: What?!

Frog: You promised.

King: Did you promise?

Princess: Yes.

Queen: Carry him to your pillow, then.

Narrator: The princess picked up the frog between her thumb and finger and oh, so carefully, put him on her pillow.

Frog: Can I have a kiss?

Princess: What?!

King: Did you promise?

Princess: No!

Queen: He is kind of cute.

Princess: What?!

Narrator:	And before anyone could stop her, the queen bent down and kissed the frog. There was a clap of thunder and puff of green smoke, which blinded them all for a minute. When the smoke cleared, there stood a wonderful prince.

Princess: Who are you?

Frog: I am the frog.

Queen: You ARE kind of cute.

Princess: I saw him first!

Narrator:	The princess and the frog prince decided to get married the very next day. And they lived happily ever after . . . once the princess got used to the frog prince's odd way of hopping about, catching flies with his tongue, and croaking instead of snoring.

—The End—

Bibliography

The Enormous Turnip

The Enormous Turnip by Kathy Parkinson (Whitman, 1986).

The Turnip by Harriet Ziefert (Viking Penguin, 1996).

The Ugly Duckling

The Ugly Duckling by Berta Hader (Gallery Books, 1990).

The Ugly Duckling by Hans Christian Andersen (Barron's, 1986).

The Ugly Duckling: A Tale from Hans Christian Andersen by Lorinda Bryan Cauley (Harcourt Brace, 1989).

The Shoemaker and the Elves

The Elves and the Shoemaker by Paul Galdone (Houghton Mifflin, 1986).

The Elves and the Shoemaker by Bernadette Watts (North-South Books, 1989).

The Shoemaker and the Elves by Ilse Plume (Harcourt Brace, 1991).

The Golden Goose

The Golden Goose by Margaret Hillert (Modern Curriculum Press, 1978).

The Golden Goose by Susan Saunders (Scholastic, 1988).

The Golden Goose by Uri Shulevitz (Farrar, Straus, & Giroux, 1995).

Rapunzel

The Arbuthnot Anthology Of Children's Literature by May Hill Arbuthnot (Scott Foresman, 1976).

Rapunzel: A Tale by the Brothers Grimm by Jutta Ash (Holt, Rinehart, & Winston, 1982).

Rapunzel by Jada Rowland (Contemporary Books, 1989).

The Princess and the Pea

The Princess and the Pea by Hans Christian Andersen (Seabury Press, 1978).

The Princess and the Pea by Sucie Stevenson (Doubleday, 1992).

The Princess and the Pea by Harriet Ziefert (Puffin, 1996).

Rumpelstiltskin

Rumpelstiltskin by Paul Galdone (Clarion, 1985).

Rumpelstiltskin by Jacob Grimm (Troll, 1979).

Rumpelstiltskin: A Tale Told Long Ago by Edith Tarcov (Four Winds, 1973).

The Emperor's New Suit

The Arbuthnot Anthology Of Children's Literature by May Hill Arbuthnot (Scott Foresman, 1976).

The Emperor's Birthday Suit by Cindy Wheeler (Random House, 1996).

The Emperor's New Clothes by Janet Stevens (Holiday, 1985).

The Frog Prince

The Frog Prince by Wilhelm Grimm (Troll, 1979).

The Frog Prince by Mary Lewis Wang (Childrens Press, 1986).

The Frog Prince, Continued by Jon Scieszka (Viking Penguin, 1991).